My Beloved Dog

PLACE YOUR PET'S I.D. OR PHOTO.

MY NAME _____

_____

PHONE _____

MY DOG'S NAME _____

_____

BIRTHDAY _____

MICROCHIP # _____

MY DOG'S HEALTH RECORD BOOK

A PRACTICAL GUIDE TO LOG YOUR DOG'S PERSONAL AND HEALTH HISTORY, WITH TIPS FOR NEW PUPPY OWNERS!!

© 2020 LEILA GRANDEMANGE

ISBN 978-0-9975658-3-6

ALL RIGHTS RESERVED

IMAGE CREDITS

Cover image dog © gollykim. Girl playing with dog © Jacklooser. Sick dog © Togatelu. Cartoon Dogs © MarinaDreams. Dog loving boy © Jacklooser. Boy picking up waste © Victor Brave. Family ©Kateryna Davydenko. Frames and stardust, Lisa Glanz. Heart Doodles courtesy of Freepik.

DISCLAIMER

THE AUTHOR IS NOT A VET. The publisher and author are not responsible nor liable for any veterinary medical advice, course of treatment, diagnosis, or any other information obtained from this book. Please consult your veterinarian with questions on how to interpret any information in this book. Thank you.

Sunny ☼ *Ville*
PUBLISHING

My Dog's

HEALTH RECORD BOOK

A PRACTICAL GUIDE TO LOG YOUR DOG'S PERSONAL AND
HEALTH HISTORY, WITH TIPS FOR NEW PUPPY OWNERS!

LEILA GRANDEMANGE

TABLE OF CONTENTS

TABLE OF CONTENTS

PART 5: DOG OWNER RESOURCES AND PRINTABLE FORMS

DOGS HAVE A WAY OF FINDING THE PEOPLE
WHO NEED THEM, AND FILLING AN EMPTINESS
WE DIDN'T EVER KNOW WE HAD.

– THOM JONES

ABOUT THE BOOK

YOUR NEW PUPPY is a loving companion that will be an important part of your life for years to come. With that in mind, you'll want to stay organized and on top of his medical history, and learn the best ways to keep your friend healthy, happy, and safe. This book was designed with that in mind.

In this book, you'll be able to record and chart your dog's personal and medical history, and find all sorts of useful puppy tips and dog owner resources to help you and your furry friend thoroughly enjoy the journey ahead. The prompts will guide you in filling out each page. Bring it with you to each vet visit. Share it with your pet sitter. Keep it handy for emergencies. Record and track your pet's personal and medical information through every season of his life!

THIS BOOK IS DIVIDED INTO 5 PARTS:

PART 1: OWNER AND DOG INFORMATION

PART 2: HEALTH CHARTS (VACCINES, GROOMING, ETC)

PART 3: VET VISIT LOG (WELLNESS EXAMS, OTHER)

PART 4: NEW PUPPY TIPS AND TRAINING

PART 5: DOG OWNER RESOURCES & PRINTABLE FORMS

A DOG IS THE ONLY THING ON EARTH THAT LOVES YOU MORE THAN HE LOVES HIMSELF.

– JOSH BILLINGS

PART 1
Owner and Dog information

HAPPINESS IS A WARM PUPPY.
– CHARLES SCHULZ

DOG OWNER INFORMATION

OWNER: _____

Phone: _____

Address:_____

E-mail: _____

Co-Owner:_____

Phone:_____

EMERGENCY CONTACTS

PRIMARY VET: _____

Emergency Vet:_____

Medical Insurance Policy: _____

Family Contact: _____

Pet Friendly Neighbor: _____

Local Shelter: _____

Animal Shelter: _____

Police: _____

Rescue Group: _____

Microchip Company: _____

Hotel that accepts Pets: _____

SEE P. 96 FOR IMPORTANT PHONE NUMBERS EVERY DOG OWNER NEEDS.

8

MY DOG'S INFORMATION

CALL NAME: _____

Registered Name: _____

Sex: _____ Born on: _____

Color/Markings: _____

Microchip # _____

Breed: _____

AKC # _____

Type of Registration: ☐ Limited ☐ Full

Other Registry # _____ DNA # _____

☐ Spayed ☐ Neutered Date: _____

MY DOG CAME FROM . . .

Breeder Name/Phone: _____

Rescue/shelter/other: _____

Date Acquired: _____

Sire: _____

Dam: _____

MY DOG'S CARE GIVERS

PRIMARY VET NAME: _____

   Phone/Email: _____

   Address: _____

Veterinary Specialists: _____

_____

_____

Pet Sitter 1: _____

_____

Pet Sitter 2: _____

_____

Groomer (Grooming log on page 25) : _____

_____

Doggie Day Care: _____

_____

Other: _____

_____

_____

_____

PET SITTER INSTRUCTION FORM

PRINT OUT THIS PAGE TO REUSE FOR EACH PET SITTER VISIT. SEE P. 90 FOR ANOTHER FORM.

MY DOG'S FEEDING SCHEDULE/ROUTINE   DATE: _____

Morning: _____

_____

Midday: _____

_____

Evening: _____

_____

SPECIAL INSTRUCTIONS FOR PET SITTER

_____

_____

_____

_____

_____

MY TRAVEL INFORMATION

Hotel/Location: _____

Contact number: _____

Leaving/Returning on: _____

Emergency contact pet sitter #2: _____

_____

11

MY DOG'S MEDICINES AND SUPPLEMENTS

Regular Medications (CHART OTHER MEDS ON PAGES 22-23)

_____

_____

Supplements: _____

_____

_____

Allergies: _____

MY DOG'S FOOD

Food brand and type (wet and/or dry; raw and/or cooked):

_____

_____

_____

_____

_____

Favorite Treats: _____

_____

MY DOG'S TRAINERS

PRIMARY TRAINING FACILITY: _____

    Phone/Email: _____

    Address: _____

Trainer 1: _____

_____

Trainer 2: _____

_____

OTHER TRAINING FACILITY: _____

    Phone/Email: _____

    Address: _____

Trainer 1: _____

_____

Trainer 2: _____

_____

Other: _____

_____

_____

MY DOG'S ACHIEVEMENTS

RECORD YOUR DOG'S ACHIEVEMENTS and milestones: training classes completed, certifications, titles, awards, tricks learned, etc.

Achievement:_____Date earned:_____

_____

Achievement:_____Date earned:_____

_____

Achievement:_____Date earned:_____

_____

Achievement:_____Date earned:_____

_____

Achievement:_____Date earned:_____

_____

Achievement:_____Date earned:_____

_____

Achievement:_____Date earned:_____

_____

Achievement:_____Date earned:_____

_____

 DOGS ARE NOT OUR WHOLE LIFE, BUT THEY MAKE OUR LIVES WHOLE.

– ROGER CARAS

PART 2
Health Charts

VACCINATION CHART

DEWORMING CHART

FECAL TEST CHART

HEARTWORM PREVENTION LOG

FLEA AND TICK CONTROL LOG

MEDICATIONS RECORD

SURGERY/HOSPITAL STAY LOG

DOG GROOMING LOG

EVERYONE THINKS THEY HAVE THE BEST
DOG. AND NONE OF THEM IS WRONG.
— W.R. PURCHE

VACCINATION CHART

Fill out this chart at your vet when your dog gets his shots.

AGE								
DATE								
DISTEMPER								
PARVOVIRUS								
ADENOVIRUS 2								
RABIES								
OTHER								

REMINDER: Complete entire puppy vaccination series because maternal antibodies can last 14-16 weeks making earlier vaccines ineffective.

NOTES: _____

_____

  16

VACCINATION CHART

Fill out this chart at your vet when your dog gets his shots.

AGE								
DATE								
DISTEMPER								
PARVOVIRUS								
ADENOVIRUS 2								
RABIES								
OTHER								

NOTES: List any notes or adverse reaction to vaccines and the date.

_____

_____

_____

DEWORMING CHART

Record the date, name of deworming product, and dosage given. Deworm and test for parasites per your vet's recommendations. SEE RESOURCE PP. 82-83.

Date	Product	Dosage

FECAL TEST CHART

Doing an annual fecal test by taking a sample of your dog's feces to your vet helps determine if specific parasites are present. Record results. SEE RESOURCE PP.82-83.

DATE	RESULTS	RECOMMENDATIONS

HEARTWORM PREVENTION LOG

Log your dog's heartworm blood testing and medication. PARASITE CONTROL TIPS P.82.

Year	Test	Jan	Feb	Mar	Apr	May	June	July	Aug	Sept	Oct	Nov	Dec

Name of product/dosage/any adverse reactions: _____

_____

  20

FLEA AND TICK CONTROL LOG

Log flea and tick products given to your dog. PARASITE CONTROL TIPS ON P. 82.

Year	Jan	Feb	Mar	Apr	May	June	July	Aug	Sept	Oct	Nov	Dec

Name of product/dosage/any adverse reactions:_____

_____

MY DOG'S MEDICATION RECORD

RECORD ALL MEDICATIONS your dog takes throughout his life. Update this page each time he changes medications or adds new ones. This will be vital information for you and your vet as your dog progresses through his treatment, or in an emergency.

NAME OF MEDICATION _____

Dosage/Frequency _____

Reason for Medication _____

Reactions if any _____

Date _____ Prescribed by _____

NAME OF MEDICATION _____

Dosage/Frequency _____

Reason for Medication _____

Reactions if any _____

Date _____ Prescribed by _____

NAME OF MEDICATION _____

Dosage/Frequency _____

Reason for Medication _____

Reactions if any _____

Date _____ Prescribed by _____

NAME OF MEDICATION _____

Dosage/Frequency _____

Reason for Medication _____

Reactions if any _____

Date _____ Prescribed by _____

MY DOG'S MEDICATION RECORD

NAME OF MEDICATION _____

Dosage/Frequency _____

Reason for Medication _____

Reactions if any _____

Date _____Prescribed by _____

NAME OF MEDICATION _____

Dosage/Frequency _____

Reason for Medication _____

Reactions if any _____

Date _____Prescribed by _____

NAME OF MEDICATION _____

Dosage/Frequency _____

Reason for Medication _____

Reactions if any _____

Date _____ Prescribed by _____

NAME OF MEDICATION _____

Dosage/Frequency _____

Reason for Medication _____

Reactions if any _____

Date _____Prescribed by _____

MY FAVORITE PET MED STORE: _____

_____

SURGERY RECORD & HOSPITAL STAYS

Record your dog's surgeries/hospital stays: i.e. dental cleaning, spay/neuter, other.

Date	Weight	Surgery/Reason for Hospital Stay	Results	Vet

MY DOG'S GROOMING LOG

Record your dog's visits to the groomer, services performed, and cost.

DATE	NAME OF GROOMER/PHONE	SERVICES DONE	COST

MY DOG'S GROOMING LOG

Record your dog's visits to the groomer, services performed, and cost.

DATE	NAME OF GROOMER/PHONE	SERVICES DONE	COST

MY DOG'S GROOMING LOG

Print this form out to reuse if you need more space.

DATE	NAME OF GROOMER/PHONE	SERVICES DONE	COST

Dogs do speak,
but only to
those who know
how to listen.

– ORHAN PAMUK

PART 3
Vet Visit Log

THIS SECTION WILL HELP YOU track your dog's health status at each stage of his life. Bring it with you to the vet. Record the reason for your visit, any questions you may have for the vet, recommendations and test results, medications prescribed, cost of the visit, and when your dog is due for his next appointment.

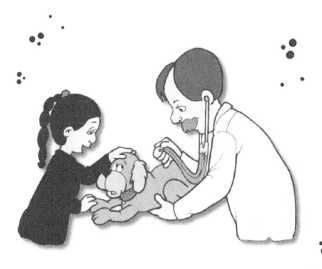

MY DOG'S WELLNESS EXAM

DATE	WEIGHT	VETERINARIAN

REASON FOR VISIT:

Annual Wellness ☐   Vaccines ☐   Dental Check ☐

Fecal Exam ☐   Heartworm Test ☐   Other (List) ☐

QUESTIONS FOR MY VET: _____

_____

_____

VETERINARY RECOMMENDATIONS: _____

_____

_____

_____

TEST RESULTS: _____

_____

MEDICATIONS PRESCRIBED: _____

_____

DUE NEXT ON: _____ COST OF VISIT: _____

NOTES: _____

_____

_____

MY DOG'S WELLNESS EXAM

DATE	WEIGHT	VETERINARIAN

REASON FOR VISIT:

Annual Wellness ☐ Vaccines ☐ Dental Check ☐

Fecal Exam ☐ Heartworm Test ☐ Other (List) ☐

QUESTIONS FOR MY VET: _____

_____

_____

VETERINARY RECOMMENDATIONS: _____

_____

_____

_____

TEST RESULTS: _____

_____

MEDICATIONS PRESCRIBED: _____

_____

DUE NEXT ON: _____ COST OF VISIT: _____

NOTES: _____

_____

_____

MY DOG'S WELLNESS EXAM

DATE	WEIGHT	VETERINARIAN

REASON FOR VISIT:

Annual Wellness ☐   Vaccines ☐   Dental Check ☐

Fecal Exam ☐   Heartworm Test ☐   Other (List) ☐

QUESTIONS FOR MY VET: _____

_____

_____

VETERINARY RECOMMENDATIONS: _____

_____

_____

_____

TEST RESULTS: _____

_____

MEDICATIONS PRESCRIBED: _____

_____

DUE NEXT ON: _____ COST OF VISIT: _____

NOTES: _____

_____

_____

MY DOG'S WELLNESS EXAM

DATE	WEIGHT	VETERINARIAN

REASON FOR VISIT:

Annual Wellness ☐   Vaccines ☐   Dental Check ☐

Fecal Exam ☐   Heartworm Test ☐   Other (List) ☐

QUESTIONS FOR MY VET: _____

_____

_____

VETERINARY RECOMMENDATIONS: _____

_____

_____

_____

TEST RESULTS: _____

_____

MEDICATIONS PRESCRIBED: _____

_____

DUE NEXT ON: _____ COST OF VISIT: _____

NOTES: _____

_____

_____

MY DOG'S WELLNESS EXAM

DATE	WEIGHT	VETERINARIAN

REASON FOR VISIT:

Annual Wellness ☐   Vaccines ☐   Dental Check ☐

Fecal Exam ☐   Heartworm Test ☐   Other (List) ☐

QUESTIONS FOR MY VET: _____

_____

_____

VETERINARY RECOMMENDATIONS: _____

_____

_____

_____

TEST RESULTS: _____

_____

MEDICATIONS PRESCRIBED: _____

_____

DUE NEXT ON: _____COST OF VISIT: _____

NOTES: _____

_____

_____

MY DOG'S WELLNESS EXAM

DATE	WEIGHT	VETERINARIAN

REASON FOR VISIT:

Annual Wellness ☐   Vaccines ☐   Dental Check ☐

Fecal Exam ☐   Heartworm Test ☐   Other (List) ☐

QUESTIONS FOR MY VET: _____

_____

_____

VETERINARY RECOMMENDATIONS: _____

_____

_____

_____

TEST RESULTS: _____

_____

MEDICATIONS PRESCRIBED: _____

_____

DUE NEXT ON: _____ COST OF VISIT: _____

NOTES: _____

_____

_____

MY DOG'S WELLNESS EXAM

DATE	WEIGHT	VETERINARIAN

REASON FOR VISIT:

Annual Wellness ☐   Vaccines ☐   Dental Check ☐

Fecal Exam ☐   Heartworm Test ☐   Other (List) ☐

QUESTIONS FOR MY VET: _____

_____

_____

VETERINARY RECOMMENDATIONS: _____

_____

_____

_____

TEST RESULTS: _____

_____

MEDICATIONS PRESCRIBED: _____

_____

DUE NEXT ON: _____ COST OF VISIT: _____

NOTES: _____

_____

_____

MY DOG'S WELLNESS EXAM

DATE	WEIGHT	VETERINARIAN

REASON FOR VISIT:

Annual Wellness ☐   Vaccines ☐   Dental Check ☐

Fecal Exam ☐   Heartworm Test ☐   Other (List) ☐

QUESTIONS FOR MY VET: _____

_____

_____

VETERINARY RECOMMENDATIONS: _____

_____

_____

_____

TEST RESULTS: _____

_____

MEDICATIONS PRESCRIBED: _____

_____

DUE NEXT ON: _____COST OF VISIT: _____

NOTES: _____

_____

_____

MY DOG'S WELLNESS EXAM

DATE	WEIGHT	VETERINARIAN

REASON FOR VISIT:

Annual Wellness ☐   Vaccines ☐   Dental Check ☐

Fecal Exam ☐   Heartworm Test ☐   Other (List) ☐

QUESTIONS FOR MY VET: _____

_____

_____

VETERINARY RECOMMENDATIONS: _____

_____

_____

_____

TEST RESULTS: _____

_____

MEDICATIONS PRESCRIBED: _____

_____

DUE NEXT ON: _____ COST OF VISIT: _____

NOTES: _____

_____

_____

MY DOG'S WELLNESS EXAM

DATE	WEIGHT	VETERINARIAN

REASON FOR VISIT:

Annual Wellness ☐   Vaccines ☐   Dental Check ☐

Fecal Exam ☐   Heartworm Test ☐   Other (List) ☐

QUESTIONS FOR MY VET: _____

_____

_____

VETERINARY RECOMMENDATIONS: _____

_____

_____

_____

TEST RESULTS: _____

_____

MEDICATIONS PRESCRIBED: _____

_____

DUE NEXT ON: _____ COST OF VISIT: _____

NOTES: _____

_____

_____

MY DOG'S WELLNESS EXAM

DATE	WEIGHT	VETERINARIAN

REASON FOR VISIT:

Annual Wellness ☐   Vaccines ☐   Dental Check ☐

Fecal Exam ☐   Heartworm Test ☐   Other (List) ☐

QUESTIONS FOR MY VET: _____

_____

_____

VETERINARY RECOMMENDATIONS: _____

_____

_____

_____

TEST RESULTS: _____

_____

MEDICATIONS PRESCRIBED: _____

_____

DUE NEXT ON: _____ COST OF VISIT: _____

NOTES: _____

_____

_____

MY DOG'S WELLNESS EXAM

DATE	WEIGHT	VETERINARIAN

REASON FOR VISIT:

Annual Wellness ☐   Vaccines ☐   Dental Check ☐

Fecal Exam ☐   Heartworm Test ☐   Other (List) ☐

QUESTIONS FOR MY VET: _____

_____

_____

VETERINARY RECOMMENDATIONS: _____

_____

_____

_____

TEST RESULTS: _____

_____

MEDICATIONS PRESCRIBED: _____

_____

DUE NEXT ON: _____ COST OF VISIT: _____

NOTES: _____

_____

_____

MY DOG'S WELLNESS EXAM

DATE	WEIGHT	VETERINARIAN

REASON FOR VISIT:

Annual Wellness ☐   Vaccines ☐   Dental Check ☐

Fecal Exam ☐   Heartworm Test ☐   Other (List) ☐

QUESTIONS FOR MY VET: _____

_____

_____

VETERINARY RECOMMENDATIONS: _____

_____

_____

_____

TEST RESULTS: _____

_____

MEDICATIONS PRESCRIBED: _____

_____

DUE NEXT ON: _____COST OF VISIT: _____

NOTES: _____

_____

_____

MY DOG'S WELLNESS EXAM

DATE	WEIGHT	VETERINARIAN

REASON FOR VISIT:

Annual Wellness ☐   Vaccines ☐   Dental Check ☐

Fecal Exam ☐   Heartworm Test ☐   Other (List) ☐

QUESTIONS FOR MY VET: _____

_____

_____

VETERINARY RECOMMENDATIONS: _____

_____

_____

_____

TEST RESULTS: _____

_____

MEDICATIONS PRESCRIBED: _____

_____

DUE NEXT ON: _____COST OF VISIT: _____

NOTES: _____

_____

_____

MY DOG'S WELLNESS EXAM

DATE	WEIGHT	VETERINARIAN

REASON FOR VISIT:

Annual Wellness ☐   Vaccines ☐   Dental Check ☐

Fecal Exam ☐   Heartworm Test ☐   Other (List) ☐

QUESTIONS FOR MY VET: _____

_____

_____

VETERINARY RECOMMENDATIONS: _____

_____

_____

_____

TEST RESULTS: _____

_____

MEDICATIONS PRESCRIBED: _____

_____

DUE NEXT ON: _____ COST OF VISIT: _____

NOTES: _____

_____

_____

MY DOG'S WELLNESS EXAM

DATE	WEIGHT	VETERINARIAN

REASON FOR VISIT:

Annual Wellness ☐　　Vaccines ☐　　Dental Check ☐

Fecal Exam ☐　　Heartworm Test ☐　　Other (List) ☐

QUESTIONS FOR MY VET: _____

_____

_____

VETERINARY RECOMMENDATIONS: _____

_____

_____

_____

TEST RESULTS: _____

_____

MEDICATIONS PRESCRIBED: _____

_____

DUE NEXT ON: _____ COST OF VISIT: _____

NOTES: _____

_____

_____

MY DOG'S WELLNESS EXAM

DATE	WEIGHT	VETERINARIAN

REASON FOR VISIT:

Annual Wellness ☐   Vaccines ☐   Dental Check ☐

Fecal Exam ☐   Heartworm Test ☐   Other (List) ☐

QUESTIONS FOR MY VET: _____

_____

_____

VETERINARY RECOMMENDATIONS: _____

_____

_____

_____

TEST RESULTS: _____

_____

MEDICATIONS PRESCRIBED: _____

_____

DUE NEXT ON: _____ COST OF VISIT: _____

NOTES: _____

_____

_____

MY DOG'S WELLNESS EXAM

DATE	WEIGHT	VETERINARIAN

REASON FOR VISIT:

Annual Wellness ☐   Vaccines ☐   Dental Check ☐

Fecal Exam ☐   Heartworm Test ☐   Other (List) ☐

QUESTIONS FOR MY VET: _____

_____

_____

VETERINARY RECOMMENDATIONS: _____

_____

_____

_____

TEST RESULTS: _____

_____

MEDICATIONS PRESCRIBED: _____

_____

DUE NEXT ON: _____COST OF VISIT: _____

NOTES: _____

_____

_____

MY DOG'S WELLNESS EXAM

Date	Weight	Veterinarian

REASON FOR VISIT:

Annual Wellness ☐   Vaccines ☐   Dental Check ☐

Fecal Exam ☐   Heartworm Test ☐   Other (List) ☐

QUESTIONS FOR MY VET: _____

_____

_____

VETERINARY RECOMMENDATIONS: _____

_____

_____

_____

TEST RESULTS: _____

_____

MEDICATIONS PRESCRIBED: _____

_____

DUE NEXT ON: _____ COST OF VISIT: _____

NOTES: _____

_____

_____

MY DOG'S WELLNESS EXAM

DATE	WEIGHT	VETERINARIAN

REASON FOR VISIT:

Annual Wellness ☐   Vaccines ☐   Dental Check ☐

Fecal Exam ☐   Heartworm Test ☐   Other (List) ☐

QUESTIONS FOR MY VET: _____

_____

_____

VETERINARY RECOMMENDATIONS: _____

_____

_____

_____

TEST RESULTS: _____

_____

MEDICATIONS PRESCRIBED: _____

_____

DUE NEXT ON: _____ COST OF VISIT: _____

NOTES: _____

_____

_____

MY DOG'S WELLNESS EXAM

DATE	WEIGHT	VETERINARIAN

REASON FOR VISIT:

Annual Wellness ☐   Vaccines ☐   Dental Check ☐

Fecal Exam ☐   Heartworm Test ☐   Other (List) ☐

QUESTIONS FOR MY VET: _____

_____

_____

VETERINARY RECOMMENDATIONS: _____

_____

_____

_____

TEST RESULTS: _____

_____

MEDICATIONS PRESCRIBED: _____

_____

DUE NEXT ON: _____ COST OF VISIT: _____

NOTES: _____

_____

_____

MY DOG'S WELLNESS EXAM

DATE	WEIGHT	VETERINARIAN

REASON FOR VISIT:

Annual Wellness ☐   Vaccines ☐   Dental Check ☐

Fecal Exam ☐   Heartworm Test ☐   Other (List) ☐

QUESTIONS FOR MY VET: _____

_____

_____

VETERINARY RECOMMENDATIONS: _____

_____

_____

_____

TEST RESULTS: _____

_____

MEDICATIONS PRESCRIBED: _____

_____

DUE NEXT ON: _____ COST OF VISIT: _____

NOTES: _____

_____

_____

MY DOG'S WELLNESS EXAM

DATE	WEIGHT	VETERINARIAN

REASON FOR VISIT:

Annual Wellness ☐   Vaccines ☐   Dental Check ☐

Fecal Exam ☐   Heartworm Test ☐   Other (List) ☐

QUESTIONS FOR MY VET: _____

_____

_____

VETERINARY RECOMMENDATIONS: _____

_____

_____

_____

TEST RESULTS: _____

_____

MEDICATIONS PRESCRIBED: _____

_____

DUE NEXT ON: _____ COST OF VISIT: _____

NOTES: _____

_____

_____

MY DOG'S WELLNESS EXAM

DATE	WEIGHT	VETERINARIAN

REASON FOR VISIT:

Annual Wellness ☐   Vaccines ☐   Dental Check ☐

Fecal Exam ☐   Heartworm Test ☐   Other (List) ☐

QUESTIONS FOR MY VET: _____

_____

_____

VETERINARY RECOMMENDATIONS: _____

_____

_____

_____

TEST RESULTS: _____

_____

MEDICATIONS PRESCRIBED: _____

_____

DUE NEXT ON: _____COST OF VISIT: _____

NOTES: _____

_____

_____

MY DOG'S WELLNESS EXAM

DATE	WEIGHT	VETERINARIAN

REASON FOR VISIT:

Annual Wellness ☐   Vaccines ☐   Dental Check ☐

Fecal Exam ☐   Heartworm Test ☐   Other (List) ☐

QUESTIONS FOR MY VET: _____

_____

_____

VETERINARY RECOMMENDATIONS: _____

_____

_____

_____

TEST RESULTS: _____

_____

MEDICATIONS PRESCRIBED: _____

_____

DUE NEXT ON: _____ COST OF VISIT: _____

NOTES: _____

_____

_____

MY DOG'S WELLNESS EXAM

DATE	WEIGHT	VETERINARIAN

REASON FOR VISIT:

Annual Wellness ☐   Vaccines ☐   Dental Check ☐

Fecal Exam ☐   Heartworm Test ☐   Other (List) ☐

QUESTIONS FOR MY VET: _____

_____

_____

VETERINARY RECOMMENDATIONS: _____

_____

_____

_____

TEST RESULTS: _____

_____

MEDICATIONS PRESCRIBED: _____

_____

DUE NEXT ON: _____COST OF VISIT: _____

NOTES: _____

_____

_____

MY DOG'S WELLNESS EXAM

PRINT OUT THIS PAGE TO REUSE IF YOUR DOG NEEDS MORE EXAM FORMS.

DATE	WEIGHT	VETERINARIAN

REASON FOR VISIT:

Annual Wellness ☐   Vaccines ☐   Dental Check ☐

Fecal Exam ☐   Heartworm Test ☐   Other (List) ☐

QUESTIONS FOR MY VET: _____

_____

_____

VETERINARY RECOMMENDATIONS: _____

_____

_____

_____

TEST RESULTS: _____

_____

MEDICATIONS PRESCRIBED: _____

_____

DUE NEXT ON: _____COST OF VISIT: _____

NOTES: _____

_____

_____

MY DOG'S WELLNESS EXAM

PRINT OUT THIS PAGE TO REUSE IF YOUR DOG NEEDS MORE EXAM FORMS.

DATE	WEIGHT	VETERINARIAN

REASON FOR VISIT:

Annual Wellness ☐   Vaccines ☐   Dental Check ☐

Fecal Exam ☐   Heartworm Test ☐   Other (List) ☐

QUESTIONS FOR MY VET: _____

_____

_____

VETERINARY RECOMMENDATIONS: _____

_____

_____

_____

TEST RESULTS: _____

_____

MEDICATIONS PRESCRIBED: _____

_____

DUE NEXT ON: _____COST OF VISIT: _____

NOTES: _____

_____

_____

MY DOG'S WELLNESS EXAM

PRINT OUT THIS PAGE TO REUSE IF YOUR DOG NEEDS MORE EXAM FORMS.

DATE	WEIGHT	VETERINARIAN

REASON FOR VISIT:

Annual Wellness ☐   Vaccines ☐   Dental Check ☐

Fecal Exam ☐   Heartworm Test ☐   Other (List) ☐

QUESTIONS FOR MY VET: _____

_____

_____

VETERINARY RECOMMENDATIONS: _____

_____

_____

_____

TEST RESULTS: _____

_____

MEDICATIONS PRESCRIBED: _____

_____

DUE NEXT ON: _____COST OF VISIT: _____

NOTES: _____

_____

_____

MY DOG'S WELLNESS EXAM

PRINT OUT THIS PAGE TO REUSE IF YOUR DOG NEEDS MORE EXAM FORMS.

DATE	WEIGHT	VETERINARIAN

REASON FOR VISIT:

Annual Wellness ☐   Vaccines ☐   Dental Check ☐

Fecal Exam ☐   Heartworm Test ☐   Other (List) ☐

QUESTIONS FOR MY VET: _____

_____

_____

VETERINARY RECOMMENDATIONS: _____

_____

_____

_____

TEST RESULTS: _____

_____

MEDICATIONS PRESCRIBED: _____

_____

DUE NEXT ON: _____ COST OF VISIT: _____

NOTES: _____

_____

_____

Properly trained, a man can be dog's best friend.

– COREY FORD

PART 4

New Puppy Tips and Training

BRINGING HOME A NEW PUPPY or adult dog is like setting off on an exciting adventure! It's also a huge responsibility, kind of like parenting a child. Below you'll find 15 tips on how to keep your fur baby happy, healthy, and safe at each stage of his life. Don't hesitate to consult a vet with questions about your dog's wellbeing.

1. PREPARE AND PUPPY PROOF: Prepare for your pups' arrival by getting the items on the NEW PUPPY CHECKLIST (P.86). Also, puppy proof your home. Move anything toxic to a dog, "chewable," or breakable out of his reach. Make sure electric cords are inaccessible and block off any part of the house you want off limits. You will also want to puppy proof your yard to ensure your dog is safe, secure, and contained. If you have a fence, check for areas that are vulnerable to chewing and digging out.

2. CHOOSE A VET ASAP: It is wise to have your pup examined by a veterinarian within the first few days of his arrival. Your vet will verify your pup's general health, set up a vaccination schedule, create an individualized wellness plan for your pet, and address any questions or concerns (i.e. diet, parasite control, spay/neuter). Keep your vet's phone number handy, as well as the number and address of the 24-hour emergency vet. IMPORTANT: LEARN THE SIGNS AND SYMPTOMS OF A SICK DOG. SEE PAGES 80-81.

3. SCHEDULE CHECK-UPS: Taking your dog to the vet at least annually allows you to verify his general health and track such things as weight, dental health, parasites, and vaccines. Never hesitate to contact your vet at once if your dog appears ill or in pain. RECORD YOUR DOG'S CHECK-UPS IN THIS BOOK, PAGES 30-59.

4. VACCINATE: Vaccinations are given to protect animals from disease, many of which can affect people (i.e. rabies). Discuss with your veterinarian the vaccine protocol that best considers the age, health, environment, and lifestyle of your puppy in order to maintain appropriate immunity. RECORD VACCINES ON PAGES 16-17.

5. CONTROL PARASITES: Parasites of dogs can cause discomfort to your dog and multiple health problems, and can also infect family members. SEE PAGES 82-83 FOR TIPS ON PARASITE CONTROL.

6. FEED A HEALTHY DIET: Not all dog foods are created equal. Choose a high-quality dog food that is best suited to your dog's size, age, and activity level. Keep feeding times regular, measure the food to prevent obesity, and always provide fresh, clean water. If you change foods, do so gradually by introducing the new food over a 7-day period by mixing the new food with the old. Learn about the pros and cons of feeding dry and/or wet; raw and/or cooked; homemade or commercial food.

7. EXERCISE YOUR DOG: Dogs need regular exercise to ensure their physical and mental health, and to prevent obesity. Exercise should be appropriate to your dog's age and energy level. Take your dog for a daily walk, throw the ball in the yard, or engage your dog in any activity that will get him up and moving. You could also call your local dog club or training center to see what activities are offered.

8. GROOM YOUR DOG REGULARLY: Dog grooming is not just about bathing and brushing your dog. It involves all aspects of canine hygiene and cleanliness including such things as cleaning ears, clipping nails, and tooth brushing. Regular grooming can be an enjoyable time of bonding, as well as alert you to possible health issues— i.e. you may discover a tick or a lump. REFER TO PAGES 74-76 FOR A LIST OF GROOMING ITEMS AND TIPS. GROOMING LOG IS ON PAGE 25.

9. POTTY TRAIN: Dogs need to relieve themselves regularly, and the younger the dog, the more often he needs to go potty. SEE RESOURCE PAGE 66-67 FOR POTTY TRAINING BASICS.

10. CRATE TRAIN: Crates are used for a variety of purposes—i.e. sleep, travel safety , potty training. SEE RESOURCE PAGES 68-69 FOR CRATE TRAINING TIPS.

BE YOUR DOG'S BEST FRIEND.

11. MAKE HOUSE RULES: Get the whole family on board. Decide what is OK and what is NOT OK in the house (i.e. jumping on sofa, sleeping in bed). Make sure everyone sticks to the rules. Consistency will help your dog grow into a well-behaved pet.

12. AVOID SEPARATION ANXIETY: Teaching your dog early on to be alone for short periods can help avoid separation anxiety. When you leave the house, try playing soft music and offering him some sturdy safe toys to keep him occupied. Leave and come home with minimum fuss so that he will learn not to worry about your coming and going. Keep in mind, dogs cannot be expected to thrive if left alone for long hours on a regular basis. Use a pet sitter, mid-day dog walker, or doggie daycare if needed.

13. TEACH BASIC OBEDIENCE: Properly done, basic obedience builds confidence, self-esteem, and it can protect your dog for life. A well-mannered dog also makes dog ownership much more enjoyable. SEE RESOURCE PAGES 70-71 FOR BASIC TRAINING TIPS.

14. KNOW CHANGING NEEDS: As your dog progresses from puppyhood through old age, his specific needs (i.e. diet, exercise) will change. Take time to learn the best ways to care for your dog's emotional and physical well-being at each stage of his life.

15. SAYING GOODBYE: Lastly, one of the most difficult aspects of pet care is saying goodbye. Due to illness and/or old age, some dogs reach a point where their quality of life is severely compromised. Electing to end the dog's life humanely is sometimes the kindest and most loving thing you can do. Your vet will be an invaluable resource as you grapple with that difficult decision.

DOGS' LIVES ARE TOO SHORT.
THEIR ONLY FAULT REALLY.

– AGNES SLIGH

A PROMISE TO MY DOG

AS A DOG OWNER, I DO SOLEMNLY SWEAR:

AKC RESPONSIBLE DOG OWNER PET PROMISE © AMERICAN KENNEL CLUB.

- I will never overlook my responsibilities for this living being and recognize that my dog's welfare is totally dependent on me.

- I will always provide fresh water and quality food for my dog.

- I will socialize my dog via exposure to new people, places, and other dogs.

- I will take pride in my dog's appearance with regular grooming.

- I will recognize the necessity of basic training by teaching my dog to reliably sit, stay and come when called.

- I will take my dog to the vet regularly and keep all vaccinations current.

- I will pick-up and properly dispose of my dog's waste.

- I will make sure my dog is regarded as an AKC Canine Good Citizen by being aware of my responsibilities to my neighbors and to the community.

- I will ensure that the proper amount of exercise and mental stimulation appropriate for my dog's age, breed and energy level is provided.

- I will ensure that my dog has some form of identification (which may include collar, tags, tattoo, or microchip ID.)

- I will adhere to local leash laws.

10 POTTY TRAINING TIPS

DOGS NEED TO relieve themselves often, and the younger the dog the more often he needs to go. By following these housetraining tips, your pup will be on his way to potty training success! Just remember, potty training a puppy takes time. So be patient.

1. **SUPERVISE:** Young pups are still developing control of their bladders and need constant supervision until they are reliably housetrained. Don't expect a puppy to be fully potty trained until he is about 6-8 months old. Even then, be aware of his needs. Each dog is different. Elderly dogs may also have trouble holding their bladder and may need to go out more often.

2. **WATCH FOR SIGNS:** Learn to read your dog's behavior and watch for signs that mean he needs to go out, such as circling and sniffing the floor right before he relieves himself. Puppies will want to relieve themselves first thing in the morning, last thing at night, after they play, nap, spend time in a crate, after chewing on a bone or toy, and after drinking. While your dog is active, take him out at least once an hour, and even more in the morning and evening.

3. **CONTAINMENT:** Teach your dog to be happy in a small room or crate when you cannot supervise him. Using a crate is a great housetraining tool because dogs will generally not eliminate in the same space where they sleep. Try placing the crate near or in your bedroom. This way you can hear if your pup whines to go out at night. Expand your dog's freedom in the house gradually.

4. **COMMIT TO A SCHEDULE:** Keep your dog on a consistent schedule for food, water, and walks while housetraining. A typical daily potty training schedule may look like this:

• *Morning routine:* Take your pup out first thing. Then, feed breakfast (aim for same time each day). Always provide fresh water. Give him 15 minutes or so to eat, and remove the bowl. Then wait between 5-30 minutes and take him out again.

• *Meal times:* Most pups eat 3-4 meals a day. Take them out right after each meal, also, after drinking water.

- *After naps and playtime:* During the day, your pup may nap every hour or so. As soon as they wake up, take them out to potty. Playtime can also give your pup the urge to potty. Keep a watchful eye for signs he wants to relieve himself.

- *Before bedtime:* Remember to take your dog out to potty one last time before you go to bed at night.

5. **CHOOSE A "POTTY SPOT":** Try to use the same door to the same area you'd like your dog to eliminate. Keep him on leash (even if yard is fenced) so that you can react quickly with a reward. Stand quietly in the chosen "potty spot." When you see him commence, use a signal or voice command (i.e. "go potty"). Once finished, offer lavish praise and a yummy treat!

6. **TRY USING A BELL:** Place a bell on the door handle and train your pup to ring the bell to go out to potty. Ring it each time you take him out. Praise your pup when he rings it on his own.

7. **PRAISE AND REWARD:** Offer enthusiastic praise ("good boy/girl!") and reward your dog when he eliminates in the right place. Never hit or yell at your dog when he has an accident. If you catch your dog in the act inside the house, make a noise to get their attention (i.e say "uh-oh") and immediately take him outside. Wait until he finishes then praise and reward.

8. **TAKE TIME TO PLAY:** After your dog eliminates, take some time to play. If you bring him in right after he goes potty, he will then learn that play-time stops when he urinates.

9. **ODOR REMOVAL:** It is especially important to remove all traces of the odor if your dog eliminates inside or else he will continue to go to that same spot to eliminate. Clean up any urine and feces in the house with enzymatic neutralizers such as *Nature's Miracle*, rather than with household detergents.

10. **PLAN AHEAD:** When leaving your pup at home, use the *month-plus-one rule* (see P.69) to know the maximun amount of time your pup can comfortably hold his bladder until your return.

8 CRATE TRAINING TIPS

CRATE TRAINING is basically giving your dog a comfy "den-like" space of his own to feel safe and secure. Crates come in various sizes, materials, and shapes, and can be used for a variety of containment purposes—sleep, travel, potty training, or in case of emergency. When used as a housetraining tool the size of the crate should be just large enough for the dog to stand up tall, turn around, fully stretch out and lie down comfortably. The limited space teaches them to hold it because dogs will naturally avoid stepping in their own waste. A crate should never be used for punishment. Your dog should associate his crate with peaceful, happy things.

Follow these tips to help you crate train your new puppy:

1. Introduce your pup to the crate gradually in small increments of time while you are home.

2. Line the crate with comfortable bedding or blankets and fill with a few sturdy safe toys. Make sure it is well ventilated and in a comfortable environment.

3. Try tossing some treats to the back of the crate or offer him his meal there. If he goes in, gently close the door for a couple of minutes and then let him back out.

4. Increase the time in the crate by 5-10-minute increments daily until you get to an hour. Keep the crate near your activities. Take your puppy outside to eliminate immediately after taking him out of his crate.

5. Speak to your dog now and then while he is learning to be in his crate. Also offer a treat to let him know he is being a good pup for calmly lying there. When it's time for you to leave him alone, you'll have a happy, calm, crate-trained dog!

6. The time spent in a crate should be limited, with regular breaks for exercise, social contact, urination, and defecation. If left too long in a crate, a dog will be forced to relieve himself on the bedding. If he does, it is because someone neglected the responsibility to take him out. It is not because he has misbehaved.

7. Use the **MONTH-PLUS-ONE RULE.** Pups cannot hold their bladder as long as an adult. If you're unsure how long your puppy can hold his bladder comfortably while in a crate (for example when you leave home to run an errand), the American Kennel club recommends using the "month-plus-one" rule: "Take the age of your puppy in months and add one, and that is the maximum number of hours that your pup should be able to comfortably hold it between potty breaks. A 3-month-old puppy plus one equals 4 hours that they should be able to stay in the crate without a mess" (Harriet Meyers, AKC.org).

8. Limited time in crates is also important for seniors and dogs with special health concerns.

. . . .

WHEN I LOOK INTO THE EYES OF AN ANIMAL,
I DO NOT SEE AN ANIMAL. I SEE A LIVING BEING.
I SEE A FRIEND. I FEEL A SOUL.

– A.D. WILLIAMS

. . . .

6 BASIC TRAINING TIPS

1. PRAISE OFTEN

The sweetest sound to a dog's ear is the sound of praise! Our happy, enthusiastic tone when we say "Yes!" or "Good boy!" is what lets our dogs know they've understood what was asked of them. The tone of our voice, yummy treats, toys, and play can all be used as forms of praise and reward. Praise your dog lavishly when he obeys you, and use positive training methods. If a dog doesn't do what you've asked, do not assume he is being disobedient. It is up to us to learn how to read a dog's body language and adjust our behavior to better communicate what we expect. That is why training classes often benefit the owner just as much, if not more, than the dog.

2. OFFER LOVING LEADERSHIP

Every dog needs a human who can lead him. But leadership is often misunderstood. It does not mean that we use force or intimidation to dominate our dog. Rather, we lead more like a partner in a dance. If you're not sure how to do that, you can consult a professional dog trainer or read a book or online article on the topic. These can help you to better understand how dogs communicate and how to train them using kind, and loving direction. This way, you can avoid training mishaps and help your pup grow into a well-trained, happy dog that's a joy to live with!

3. TEACH BASIC COMMANDS

Whether you enroll in formal training or not, every dog needs to learn basic commands—*Come, Heel, Sit, Stay, and Down.* Discuss with your vet the best timing (based on your pup's vaccine schedule), to enroll in puppy kindergarten. Go loaded with praise and treats, and enjoy your puppy. Consider going further by enrolling in more advanced obedience classes. TO LEARN MORE: DOWNLOAD YOUR FREE AKC EBOOK AT WWW.AKC.ORG CALLED, "THE FIVE COMMANDS EVERY DOG SHOULD KNOW."

4. KEEP THINGS SHORT AND SWEET

Puppies have short attention spans and can burn out if trained for too long. Set your pup up for success by keeping sessions 1-2 minutes. Try mini training sessions throughout your day. Keep it fun and set reasonable expectations for each mini session. Always end on a positive note, with praise, treats, or play time.

5. PLAY WITH YOUR DOG

Playing with your dog is a great way to teach him to obey. It is also one of the best ways to keep him happy and healthy. It's good for owners too! Playing with your pooch should always be a positive experience. Try various games such as fetch, hide-and-seek, find-the-treat, tug of war, swimming, Frisbee, and soccer, and discover what you and your dog are good at.

These are a few of the benefits of playing with your dog:

- Using play, combined with reward and treats is a great way to encourage good behavior.
- Prevents boredom and destructive behavior by providing the opportunity for mental and physical stimulation. Dogs love having the chance to use their instinctive behaviors such as running, jumping, sniffing, and searching for things.
- Strengthens the bond between you and your pet, encourages communication, and creates loyalty.
- Running, chasing, jumping, and swimming can help keep your dog fit, build muscle, and prevent obesity and diabetes.

6. PARTICIPATE IN ACTIVITIES WITH YOUR DOG

Numerous organizations such as the American Kennel Club offer activities and sports for dogs. Here are a few: Obedience, Agility, Conformation, Rally, Freestyle, Tracking, Field Events, and Pet Therapy. Also check with your local dog clubs and training centers for a list of activities, meet-ups, and classes. There are also more simple pleasures to enjoy with your dog such as taking a walk in the park, jogging, swimming, or simply playing in the yard.

SOCIALIZING YOUR PUPPY, Q & A

WHAT IS SOCIALIZATION? Socialization is the ongoing process in which a puppy is strategically introduced to things he may encounter as an adult, such as new people, animals, stimuli, and environments. Ideally, this process begins at birth and continues throughout a dog's life. The following Q & A is a brief overview of the process of socialization.

- **When do I begin?** The first three months of life is the prime window of opportunity for pups to experience new things because it's the period when sociability outweighs fear. Begin as soon as you bring your puppy home. Start gently in your home in spaces your pup feels secure, but steadily build up to new challenges. Encourage your puppy to explore and investigate at his own pace while under your watchful eye. As he gets older, he will visit other homes to get used to new people, sights, smells, and sounds. Eventually he will graduate to quiet public places followed by more busy public places like a downtown shopping area.

- **When can my puppy begin socialization classes?** Today it is widely acknowledged that isolation between 8 and 16 weeks old can contribute to behavior problems. For this reason, the American Veterinary Society of Animal Behavior (WWW.AVSAB.ORG) states that puppies can start puppy socialization classes as early as 7-8 weeks of age as long as they are up to date on vaccines and disease and parasite free. Puppies should receive a minimum of one set of vaccines at least 7 days prior to the first class and a first deworming. They should be kept up to date on vaccines throughout the class. The AVSAB also advises that visits to dog parks and areas that are not sanitized and/or highly trafficked by dogs of unknown vaccination or disease status should be avoided.

- **What are some things I can do to socialize my puppy?** Puppies should be handled early on and learn to accept being touched on all parts of their body. Efforts should be made to expose pups gradually to as many different people, well-socialized animals, situations, places, etc. as possible. Introduce your puppy to a variety of interactive toys and games, steps, tunnels, and a variety of surfaces to enrich his environment, and take your puppy on as many car trips as possible. Always check with your vet before enrolling your puppy in socialization classes. Training should be focused on the use of positive reinforcement with frequent rewards and praise—petting, play and/or treats.

- **Can I plan a puppy party?** Inviting friends with vaccinated, well-mannered dogs can be a fun way to introduce your puppy to other dogs in a relaxed yet controlled setting. Keep puppy parties small, short and sweet to begin (about a half hour). Later, you can increase to 1 hour and enlarge your parties to include small children and more adults. Ask guests to give your puppy bits of his favorite treat to help imprint in his mind that being around people can be rewarding and lots of fun!

- **What if I adopted an older pup or adult that was not socialized? Is it too late?** It may be a bit harder, but by no means impossible, especially with the help of an experienced trainer. Behavior issues (i.e. fear, aggression) in social settings must be addressed in all dogs.

Puppy Play Date!

DOG GROOMING BASICS

IF YOU USE A PROFESSIONAL DOG GROOMER, YOU CAN LOG VISITS ON PP. 25-27.

DOG GROOMING IS much more than bathing and brushing your dog. Dog grooming involves all aspects of canine hygiene and cleanliness. You can pay for grooming services or try to do them yourself. If you'd like to try yourself, the following tips cover the basics and will get you started. DOWNLOAD YOUR FREE AKC EBOOK AT WWW.AKC.ORG CALLED "THE ALL-PURPOSE GROOMING TOOL KIT."

10 ESSENTIAL DOG GROOMING ITEMS:

- **Dog brush:** Brushes fall into 4 main categories: regular brushes, combs, rakes and deshedding tools. The type you use will depend on your dog's coat. See #2 on the next page for more information.

- **A good comb.** Helps to remove tangles. You may also want a flea comb to check for fleas and ticks.

- **Coat spray:** Reduces static while brushing and helps grooming tools glide more easily through fur. Many sprays also condition the coat and leave a pleasant scent.

- **Dog shampoo and conditioner,** and bath wipes for a quick clean up.

- **Drying Supplies:** A dog blow dryer and microfiber towels.

- **Ear cleaning solution.**

- **Dog toothbrush and toothpaste.**

- **Dog nail clippers** or nail grinder, and styptic powder.

- **Animal grooming clippers** and/or shears to trim long hair.

- **Grooming Table with arm:** Not essential, but nice to have.

DOG GROOMING BASICS:

1. KEEP IT FUN: The most important tip is to keep grooming times enjoyable for both you and your dog. Schedule these times when your dog is relaxed. Keep the sessions short (5-10 minutes) while your puppy is young, and gradually lengthen the time as he gets older until it becomes a routine. Teach your dog to be comfortable getting touched all over his body. This will be useful when you need to clip his nails or clean his ears, or for a vet exam. Praise your pup throughout the session and offer a delicious treat when it's over!

2. BRUSHING: Regular grooming with a brush or comb will help to keep your dog's fur in good condition. Brushing removes dirt and spreads the natural oils in the coat. It also prevents tangles and keeps the skin clean and irritant-free. Dogs with a smooth, short coat may only need to be brushed once a week. Use a *Bristle Brush* to remove any dead fur, and a *Slicker Brush* for tangles. Comb through the tail and longer furnishings,and don't forget to trim the fur around the hocks and feet. This is also a great time to check for fleas and ticks. Some dogs require clipping or sculpting. Seek the assistance of a professional dog groomer if needed. GROOMING LOG ON P.25.

3. BATHING: Bathing your dog every 2-3 months or so is recommended. Dogs that spend more time outdoors may require more frequent bathing. Always use a gentle shampoo that is safe for dogs. Before the bath, give your dog a good brushing to remove dead fur and mats. Place a rubber mat in your bath to prevent your dog from slipping, and fill the tub with 3-4 inches of lukewarm water. Use a spray hose or a large plastic pitcher to wet your dog, taking care not to spray directly in the ears, eyes, or nose. Gently massage the shampoo working from head to tail, always being careful to keep shampoo away from the eyes. Rinse well. Don't forget to check the ears for any foul odor or debris. Use an *ear cleaner* made for dogs if needed. Finish off by towel drying your dog or using a blow dryer. Carefully monitor the heat level to ensure it's not too hot.

4. SPECIAL BREEDS: Dogs with loose facial skin/wrinkles, such as sharp-pei or pugs, will need special attention. Clean the folds with a damp washcloth to prevent dirt and bacteria from causing irritation or infection. Thoroughly dry the areas between the folds.

5. LONG EARS: Dogs with long or droopy ears need their ears checked weekly. Look inside the dog's ear to ensure they are clean and free of foul odor. Remove wax and dirt from your pet's ears with a cotton ball moistened with a gentle ear cleaner. Some breeds, such as poodles, require the removal of excess hair leading into the ear canal. Ask your vet or a groomer for guidance if needed.

6. NAIL CLIPPING: While your dog is still a puppy, get him used to having his feet touched. Try given him a daily foot massage. Once he is used to this, use quality nail trimmers to cut off the tip of each nail at a slight angle, just before the point where it begins to curve. Take care to avoid *the quick*— the blood vessel that runs into the nail. The quick is a pink area that can be seen through the nail. In dogs with black nails the quick is harder to see. If you accidentally cut the quick, it may bleed, in which case you can use some *styptic powder* to stop the bleeding. Don't forget to clip the dew claws, because they do not come into contact with the ground and can easily grow long and become uncomfortable for a dog. Once the nails are cut, you could use an emery board to smooth the rough edges. YouTube has some useful videos to guide you. An alternate method of trimming nails is by using a *nail grinder.* This rotary tool sands down the nail without risk of cutting too close to the quick.

7. TOOTH BRUSHING: Dental disease, especially periodontal disease, is one of the most common diseases in our canine companions. Fortunately, dental disease can be reduced and even prevented with regular tooth brushing. Use a *soft-bristled toothbrush* and *toothpaste* made for dogs. Human toothpastes and baking soda can present dangers for our pets. Begin by letting your dog taste the flavored toothpaste, and then run your finger along the gums of the upper teeth. Repeat this process with a toothbrush (should take about 30 seconds). Work from back to front, making small circles along the gum lines. Keep sessions short and offer praise and treats. Brush his teeth a couple of times a week, or daily if possible, to help him get used to it. Dental sprays are also available to help prevent tartar build up. Even with the best tooth brushing, some dogs may still need an occasional professional cleaning. Your dog's dental health should be evaluated yearly by your vet.

8. ANAL GLANDS: Last, but not least, check your dog's bottom area to ensure it is clean. Also, make sure there is no swelling as anal gland abscesses often go unnoticed in the early stages. Sometimes dogs will scoot their bottoms on the ground, which indicates they may be having a problem. If there is a concern, call your vet. Some groomers will offer to check the anal gland's and empty them.

15 PET SAFETY TIPS

1. **MAKE SURE YOUR DOG HAS IDENTIFICATION.** Your dog should have an identification tag with your name, address, and phone number. Also consider permanent identification such as a Microchip or Tattoo. These can be invaluable in recovering your pet in the unfortunate situation that your dog becomes lost. DON'T FORGET TO REGISTER YOUR DOG'S MICROCHIP (OR TATTOO) ONCE IT IS IMPLANTED.

2. **KEEP YOUR DOG CONTAINED.** Is your yard safe and secure? A fenced yard is a huge plus in keeping your dog safe. Walk around the border regularly to ensure there are no holes and openings for your dog to slip out. If you do not have the possibility to fence your yard, you'll want to consider other options. Some folks use a dog run or invisible fence. Keep in mind that invisible fences may keep your dog in, but they do not keep intruders out. Always watch your pet regardless of your type of fence. For properties without a fence (i.e., city dwellers), stress to all family members that the dog must be leashed when taken outdoors.

3. **DOG PROOF YOUR HOME.** Are all dangerous products and electrical cords out of your dog's reach? Is the toilet seat cover down? Are there any garden plants that may be toxic to your dog in the house or yard? These are some of the many questions you will want to ask before bringing a dog home, and throughout his life.

4. **PICK UP YOUR DOG'S WASTE.** Infectious dog diseases and parasites can be transmitted via fecal matter. Keep your dog and others safe by picking up and properly disposing of your dog's waste. Don't forget to take along some dog waste bags when you take your dog for a walk.

5. **RESPECT LEASH LAWS.** Leash laws were created to protect the public, as well as your dog and other dogs. Be aware of leash laws and keep your dog restrained in those areas where it is required.

6. TOY SAFETY. Provide your dog with a variety of sturdy and safe toys. Avoid toys with stuffing, as dogs can chew these open and swallow the stuffing. Considering that, toys with glass or plastic eyes should also be avoided. Never leave a dog unattended with a toy that has small, detachable, or broken parts. Discard damaged toys and replace with new ones.

7. PROVIDE GOOD SHELTER. Ideally, a dog will sleep in the home of his owner. If however your dog spends a lot of time outside, make sure that he has plenty of shade in the summer, warmth in the winter, and appropriate shelter.

8. NEVER LEAVE YOUR PET IN THE CAR ON WARM DAYS. A temperature that feels only a little warm for a person might be too hot for a dog. Remember that he is wearing a fur coat. Even days that average 70° can be too hot for a dog, even with the car widow cracked. Dogs can quickly succumb to heat stress. Also, avoid walking your dog midday during a heat wave. Choose a cooler time of day. Signs of heatstroke include excessive panting and drooling, anxiety, weakness, and abnormal gum color (darker red or even purple). Heat stroke might even result in collapse and even death. All dogs that spend time outside need access to shade and plenty of cool, fresh drinking water.

9. TRAVEL SAFE. During travel, dogs should be either in a crate, or attached in a car seat designed for dogs with seat belt and harness. Never let your dog hang his head out a car window or ride in the back of a pick-up truck.

10. PREPARE FOR A DISASTER. Fire, flood, hurricanes, earthquakes, sudden illness, or injury can happen at any time. Be prepared. Keep an emergency kit handy. This should include a copy of your dog's health/vaccine records, clean water, enough food for a few days, food and water bowl, an extra collar and leash, and first aid equipment. Have a list of animal shelters, hotels, and places that allow dogs. REFER TO THE PET DISASTER CHECKLIST ON PAGE 94.

11. KNOW BASIC FIRST AID FOR DOGS. What would you do if your pet gets a cut or wound, a burn, or if he ingests a harmful chemical? What if he has a seizure, or is found choking or goes into shock?

Or what if you find a tick on him? Having some basic first aid knowledge and being equipped with the right tools can be invaluable in reducing the severity of an injury. It can also buy time until you can get to a vet. Have a pet first aid kit handy. You can purchase a pre-made kit or build your own. Call and/or visit your vet when needed. SEE RESOURCE P. 93 FOR A LIST OF PET FIRST AID ITEMS.

12. FIND A PET SITTER. Make sure you have someone to care for your dog in case you need to go away. Give the sitter all your dog's important information (i.e. this record book, rabies certificate, vet number) in case your dog gets sick or lost. Have the number of a good boarding kennel or doggie daycare if needed. PET SITTER INSTRUCTION PRINTABLE FORMS ARE ON PAGES 90-91.

13. KEEP AN EMERGENCY CONTACT LIST. Keep a list of people who have agreed to care for your dog in case of sudden illness, hospitalization, or another emergency. Leave this list, as well as general care instructions, in a safe and visible place.
SEE PAGE 8 TO RECORD YOUR EMERGENCY PHONE CONTACTS.
SEE PP. 96-97 FOR PHONE NUMBERS EVERY DOG OWNER NEEDS TO KNOW.

14. MAKE A WILL. It is wise to keep a document stating the arrangements you've made for your pets in the event of your death.

15. KEEP A CURRENT PHOTO. Keep a good, clear, and current photo of your dog readily available in the event your dog is lost. If you have a smart phone, save the photo to your phone. Know what to do if you lose your dog. SEE RESOURCE PAGE 95 TO LEARN THE FIVE THINGS TO DO IF YOU HAVE LOST YOUR DOG.

TIP: IF YOU HAVE A SMART PHONE, SAVE A CURRENT CLEAR PHOTO OF YOUR DOG IN CASE HE GETS LOST.

6 SIGNS & SYMPTOMS OF A SICK DOG

NO ONE LIKES TO THINK about their dog becoming sick, but if your dog is showing signs of illness, it's important to get him to a veterinarian right away. Look for these symptoms to find out if your dog is sick or injured. Always consult a vet when needed.

RECORD YOUR DOG'S SURGERY OR HOSPITAL STAYS ON PAGE 24.

LOG YOUR DOG'S VET VISITS ON PAGES 30-59.

1. DIARRHEA, VOMITING, UNUSUAL URINATION

Dogs may vomit for a variety of reasons, and it's not always a sign that something is wrong. However, if vomiting or diarrhea is persistent, or very frequent, contact your vet immediately—Diarrhea that continues past 24 hours and/or has blood (red or black) could be a sign of many GI diseases, some potentially serious, especially if accompanied by decreased appetite or vomiting. Conversely, your dog may also suffer from constipation. Contact your vet if your pet's bowel movements become irregular or infrequent. If you notice your dog is suddenly urinating indoors or urinating very frequently, this may also be a symptom of illness.

2. PROBLEMS WITH THE EYES OR EARS

Checking your dog's eyes or ears is one of the easiest ways to tell something is wrong with him. Look for cloudiness in the eyes, constant tearing, or a yellow discharge. If your dog seems unable to see where he is going, there may be a problem with his eyes. If you notice your pet shaking his head and scratching his ears a lot, especially when accompanied by a strong smell, it may be a sign of infection.

3. IRREGULAR BREATHING

Irregular breathing may be anything from coughing, sneezing, wheezing, or panting. These can all be signs of various ailments, such as being overheated or overworked. It could also mean your dog is cold.

4. CHANGES IN ENERGY LEVELS

Just like us, dogs' energy levels increase and decrease daily depending on factors such as weather or activity. However, when symptoms like your pet sleeping more than normal, seeming lethargic, acting restless or pacing last more than a day or two, they may be cause for concern.

5. WEAKNESS IN LIMBS

Keep an eye out for any limping, repeated tripping, or loss of balance. All of these may be signs of serious injury or illness.

6. CHANGES IN EATING

A dog refusing meals or eating less than usual may be cause for concern, along with dogs whose appetite suddenly increases.

CAUTION: If you suspect that your dog may have a contagious disease (i.e. Parvovirus), call your vet. They may ask you to enter their facility from a special entrance to protect others from possible contamination.

 TIP: A DOG'S NORMAL TEMPERATURE RANGES FROM 99-102.5 °F. NEVER HESITATE TO CONTACT YOUR VET FOR GUIDANCE.

I WISH PEOPLE WOULD REALIZE THAT ANIMALS ARE TOTALLY DEPENDENT ON US, HELPLESS, LIKE CHILDREN, A TRUST THAT IS PUT UPON US.

– JAMES HERRIOT

6 PARASITE CONTROL TIPS

PARASITES OF DOGS CAN CAUSE multiple health problems, including heartworm disease, skin allergies, gastrointestinal disease, and tick-borne diseases such as Lyme. Some of these parasites can also infect family members. Several factors come into play when choosing how often/when/if to administer a product. Discuss with your vet the best protocol for your dog. The following tips and preventative measures will help to protect your dog and enhance your family's enjoyment of your pet.

1. FECAL EXAMS: Doing an annual fecal test by testing a sample of your dog's feces at your vet can help to determine if specific parasites are present. RECORD FECAL TESTS AND RESULTS ON PAGE 19.

2. HEARTWORM: Heartworm is a mosquito-borne illness that causes lung and heart disease in dogs. Prevention is simple and relatively inexpensive with a monthly pill or chewable. Heartworm preventatives can also provide protection from some or all of the most common intestinal parasites. It is important not to begin heartworm prevention medication unless your dog has already consistently been on the monthly prevention, or until the heartworm test result is reported as negative. An annual heartworm blood test is recommended by the American Heartworm Society to screen for heartworm disease. RECORD YOUR HEARTWORM PREVENTIVE MEDICINES ON PAGE 20.

3. INTESTINAL PARASITES: Intestinal parasites, including round worms, hookworms, and whipworms, are passed to dogs through infected feces. Humans are also susceptible to some of these parasites. Ask your vet for guidance in choosing the proper medication and dosage for your dog. RECORD DEWORMING ON P. 18.

4. FLEAS AND TICKS: Keeping ticks off your dog and family is especially important. Learn the proper way to remove a tick (see the following recommendations from the cdc.gov). It is advisable to keep a tick remover on hand and in your dog first aid kit.

Never hesitate to consult a vet for guidance in tick removal. Serious illnesses such as Lyme disease and Ehrlichiosis are all common tick-borne diseases shared by dogs and humans. Based on where you live, your vet will recommend a preventative product. He will also advise which months are most appropriate to administer it. LOG YOUR FLEA/TICK TREATMENTS ON PAGE 21.

HOW TO REMOVE A TICK (FROM THE CDC.GOV)
1. Use fine-tipped tweezers to grasp the tick as close to the skin's surface as possible.
2. Pull upward with steady, even pressure. Don't twist or jerk the tick; this can cause the mouth-parts to break off and remain in the skin. If this happens, remove the mouth-parts with tweezers. If you are unable to remove the mouth easily with clean tweezers, leave it alone and let the skin heal.
3. After removing the tick, thoroughly clean the bite area and your hands with rubbing alcohol or soap and water.
4. Never crush a tick with your fingers. Dispose of a live tick by putting it in alcohol, placing it in a sealed bag/container, wrapping it tightly in tape, or flushing it down the toilet.

5. PICK UP YOUR DOG'S FECES: Children love to run through the yard barefoot, and put things in their mouth. Be certain that pet feces are picked up at least daily and that play areas and sandboxes are covered to prevent animals from soiling them. Toxocara (a type of roundworm) can be acquired from soil contaminated with the feces of cats and dogs. Do not allow infants to eat dirt or put food or foreign objects from the ground in their mouth.

6. WASH HANDS: After any exposure to soil, sandboxes, or raw meat, wash your hands well. Also, wash children's hands, and your own, after playing with pets.

ALWAYS PICK UP AFTER YOUR DOG.

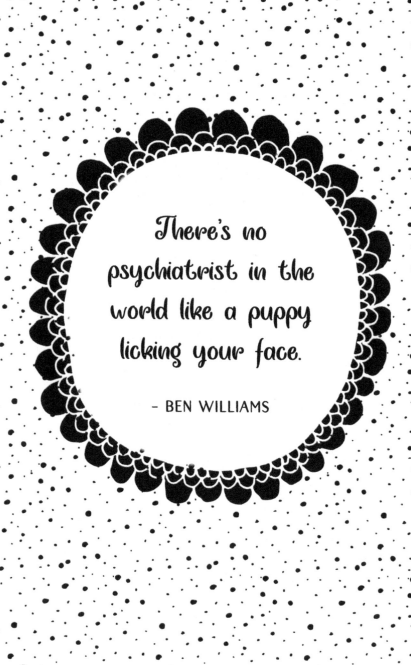

There's no psychiatrist in the world like a puppy licking your face.

– BEN WILLIAMS

PART 5
Resources and Printable Forms

NEW PUPPY CHECKLIST

YOU CAN PRINT THIS PAGE AND TAKE IT WITH YOU PET SHOPPING.

CONGRATULATIONS ON YOUR NEW PUPPY! If you don't already have these items, you'll want to add them to your shopping list to help keep your puppy happy, healthy, and safe.

- ☐ **Dog Collar:** This holds your pup's license and ID tag. Choose a soft adjustable collar for a young puppy, and then a larger one as he grows older.

- ☐ **Leash:** Choose a leash that has a loop that is easy to grip. At least one 4-6-foot leash and an additional longer lead for training.

- ☐ **Identification:** Tag with your name and address. A Microchip is also recommended.

- ☐ **Food and Water Bowls:** Stainless steel bowls are a good choice. Wash daily.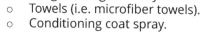

- ☐ **Containment:** Crate, puppy pen, dog gate(s).

- ☐ **Dog Toys:** Choose age specific toys and chew toys. Only offer your puppy strong, durable, well-made toys that are sized appropriately. Remove damaged toys immediately!

- ☐ **Dog Food and Training Treats:** Food should be appropriate for your dog's developmental stage.

- ☐ **Bedding and Snuggle Blanket:** Soft, warm, and cozy! At least 2 sets. Wash regularly.

- ☐ **Cleaning Supplies:** Use "enzymatic cleaners" to help remove urine and feces odors in case your dog has a potty accident indoors.

- ☐ **Dog Grooming Items:** (see P.74 for grooming basics). You may need some or all of these items depending on your breed of dog:
    - o Dog shampoo and conditioner.
    - o Pet grooming blow dryer.
    - o Towels (i.e. microfiber towels).
    - o Conditioning coat spray.
    - o Soft-bristle brush and metal comb.
    - o Ear cleaning solution.
    - o Dog toothbrush and toothpaste.
    - o Dog nail grinder or nail clippers (and styptic powder).
    - o Animal grooming clippers and/or shears to trim long hair.

NEW PUPPY EXTRAS

JOT DOWN ANY EXTRA ITEMS you'd like to get for your new furry friend, such as special toys, dog training books, recommended dog food/treats, cute dog clothes, grooming table with arm, etc.

_____

_____

_____

_____

_____

_____

_____

_____

_____

_____

_____

_____

_____

_____

_____

_____

_____

_____

_____

PET TRAVEL CHECKLIST

BEFORE LEAVING ON A TRIP with your dog, you'll want to verify a few things: Discuss with your vet any health risks at your destination (i.e. heartworm) and make sure your dog is healthy for travel. Call ahead to ensure your lodging is "pet friendly," familiarize yourself with the hotel rules/fees, and always clean up after your pet. If you' re traveling by plane, find out their requirements for pet travel. FOR MORE INFORMATION ON PET TRAVEL, VISIT PETTRAVEL.COM. SEE PP.98-99 FOR MORE PET TRAVEL WEBSITES.

Keep this pet travel checklist handy while you're packing:

- ☐ **Identification.** Bring ID tags, license numbers, tattoo, and microchip numbers for your pet.
- ☐ **Emergency numbers.** Print out a list of veterinary offices and emergency clinics where you're traveling. Have your vet's phone #.
- ☐ **Collar and Leash.** Bring a spare set in case one brakes.
- ☐ **Crate/carrier**/harness/seat belt clip for travel. Some hotels require you to crate your pet when you are out of the room.
- ☐ **Comfort items.** Favorite blanket, bedding, toys, and chew items.
- ☐ **Clean up.** Poop bags/ litter box and scoop/ piddle pads.
- ☐ **Food,** bottled water, and treats. You may also need a can opener.
- ☐ **Bowls.** Food and Water bowls.
- ☐ **Cleaning supplies,** i.e. paper towels, disinfectant wipes, lint roller.
- ☐ **Extra sheets and towels.** Cover furniture and bedding to protect from your dog.
- ☐ **Health Certificate.** If required, this is obtained from your vet.
- ☐ **Copy of shot records.** Make sure to includes the rabies certificate.
- ☐ **Medications**/supplements/preventatives. Bring copies of your pet's prescriptions in case you need refills.
- ☐ **Pet First Aid Kit.** You can make a kit yourself or purchase one online.
- ☐ **Pet Insurance** and claims forms.
- ☐ **Photo.** A recent photo of your dog.
- ☐ **Grooming Tools,** such as brush/comb, nail clippers, and toothbrush.

MY PET TRAVEL TO-DO LIST

YOU CAN PRINT THIS PAGE TO REUSE EACH TIME YOU TRAVEL.

If you're traveling with your pet, there's always lots to do. Use this form to help you prepare and stay on track. Happy travels!

TRIP/DATE:_____

Hotel Rules/Fees: _____

Things to-do/Pet things to bring:

☐ _____

☐ _____

☐ _____

☐ _____

☐ _____

☐ _____

☐ _____

☐ _____

☐ _____

☐ _____

☐ _____

☐ _____

☐ _____

☐ _____

THE JOURNEY OF LIFE IS SWEETER
WHEN TRAVELED WITH A DOG.

– AUTHOR UNKNOWN

PET SITTER INSTRUCTION FORM

THIS PAGE CAN BE PRINTED OUT AND REUSED FOR EACH PET SITTER VISIT.

MY DOG'S FEEDING SCHEDULE/ROUTINE   DATE: _____

Morning : _____

_____

Midday : _____

_____

Evening : _____

_____

SPECIAL INSTRUCTIONS FOR PET SITTER

_____

_____

_____

_____

_____

MY TRAVEL INFORMATION
Hotel/Location: _____

Contact Number: _____

Leaving/Returning on: _____

Emergency Contact Pet Sitter #2: _____

PET SITTER NOTES (7-DAY CHART)

THIS PAGE CAN BE PRINTED OUT AND REUSED FOR EACH PET SITTER VISIT.

TO MY PET SITTER: Please use this form to record day/times of visits and any observations or concerns you may have about my pets. Thank you.

BEST NUMBER TO REACH ME: _____

DATE	TIME/AM	TIME/NOON	MIDDAY	TIME/PM	OBSERVATIONS/CONCERNS

NOTES:_____

_____

CHILDREN & SAFETY AROUND DOGS

TEACH CHILDREN THE FOLLOWING 10 SAFETY RULES.

1. Teach children that a dog is not a toy. Explain that they need to be gentle when interacting with a dog (i.e. never pull tail or ears or rough house).

2. Teach children how to approach and pet a dog nicely.

3. Teach children never to invade a dog's space, and never to sneak up on a dog. A frightened dog could bite.

4. Teach children to let your dog eat undisturbed. Some dogs can become defensive around their food.

5. Teach children never to take a bone or toy from a dog's mouth. Some dogs are possessive of their toys.

6. Teach children how to observe and understand a dog's body language. A dog will give warning signs when he is being bothered. Some of these signs include growling/barking, showing teeth, hair standing, ears back, tail up. Warn children that if they see those signs not to scream, run, or stare into the dog's eyes. Teach them to walk away slowly, no fast movements.

7. Teach children to tell an adult immediately if a dog or any other animal bites them.

8. Teach children never to get near dogs that are fighting or try to break them up. They should call an adult for help.

9. Teach children to wash their hands after playing with a dog. It is also unwise to let a dog lick a child's face.

10. Teach children always to ask an owner's permission before petting his dog.

REMINDER: As a general rule, children should never be left unsupervised with a dog. DOWNLOAD THE ONLINE PDF OF "AKC'S SAFETY AROUND DOGS PROGRAM FOR KIDS OF ALL AGES," AT WWW.AKC.ORG.

FIRST AID KIT FOR PETS

BE PREPARED for the most common pet injuries. You can purchase a ready made first-aid kit or you can put one together using the following guide.

PORTABLE FIRST AID KIT FOR PETS (Adapted from the American Kennel Club, AKC.org):

- ☐ Water-proof storage container for kit.
- ☐ Antiseptic/anti-bacterial cleansing wipes/Alcohol prep pads.
- ☐ Eye wash.
- ☐ Eye and skin wash in one.
- ☐ A sock (foot wrapper).
- ☐ Latex surgical gloves.
- ☐ Electrolyte powder (add to water on hot days).
- ☐ Emergency space blanket.
- ☐ Small flashlight.
- ☐ Bottled water.
- ☐ Medicated balm.
- ☐ Leash and collar.
- ☐ Soft muzzle.
- ☐ Speak to your vet about what to pack in case your dog has a sudden allergic reaction.
- ☐ Flexible bandage.
- ☐ Gauze roll.
- ☐ Blunt bandage scissor (to cut gauze and to clip hair around wounds).
- ☐ Electric clippers (to trim fur around wounds).
- ☐ Wood splint.
- ☐ Paper towels.
- ☐ Blanket or clean towel (to keep your dog warm, restrain, or to use as a stretcher).
- ☐ Plastic baggies.
- ☐ Small cold pack and hot pack (self-activating).
- ☐ Cotton swabs.
- ☐ Antibiotic ointment/packets.
- ☐ A rectal thermometer.
- ☐ Blunt-tipped tweezers or hemostat (to remove foreign objects).
- ☐ Tick remover.
- ☐ Space for copy of dog's papers & vet records (sealed in plastic bag).
- ☐ Card with your veterinary emergency clinic phone number and the local or national poison-control number.

PET DISASTER EVACUATION CHECKLIST

ANIMALS ARE AFFECTED by the same emergencies and natural disasters as people. Having a pre-determined plan and being prepared will help you think clearly and stay calm. Visit the avma.org to learn more about pets and disaster preparedness.

EVACUATION CHECKLIST FOR PETS (Adapted from AKC.org):

- ☐ Dog medicines(s), i.e. heart worm, flea, ear mite medicine, etc.
- ☐ Dog Bowls
- ☐ Dog Food (1-week minimum, 2-week suggested), dog treats, etc.
- ☐ Can opener
- ☐ Leashes: walking leash, short leash
- ☐ Harness (to attach to seat belt)
- ☐ Extra dog tag, (masking tape, laundry pen)
- ☐ Cell #, Hotel #, and Room #
- ☐ Pet records stored in waterproof container or plastic sealable bag
- ☐ Crate
- ☐ Dog bed/blanket/toys
- ☐ Supplies/paper towels, rug cleaner, toilettes, towels, flashlight
- ☐ Current dog photograph(s) with your notification information: useful for fliers should your dog go missing or must be left at shelter
- ☐ Dog friendly hotel listings/telephone lists
- ☐ Shampoo/grooming items
- ☐ Litter/portable litter pan
- ☐ Duct tape
- ☐ Bottled water
- ☐ Pet First Aid Kit

EMERGENCY DISASTER HOTLINE (800) 227-4645.

94

5 THINGS TO DO IF YOU HAVE LOST A DOG

1. Immediately put out food, water and your dog's bed or an article of your choice at the location where your dog was last seen. There's a good chance that your dog may return.
2. Get the word out by using flyers and signs (like yard sales signs) with a picture of your dog and your phone number, and then check your phone often! Go door-to-door with flyers in the neighborhood where your dog was last seen.
3. Contact your local animal shelter and animal control facilities, vet clinics and police departments to report your dog missing. Fax or e-mail them a photo of your dog and your contact information.
4. Instruct everyone that is helping you NOT to call or chase your dog. This will prolong your search. If they see your dog, tell them to sit or lay down (no eye contact) and gently toss out tasty treats to lure your dog in.
5. Post your dog on your local craigslist, in your local paper and on other lost and found internet/Facebook sites

5 THINGS TO DO IF YOU HAVE FOUND A DOG

1. Check for a license or ID tag. No tags? Ask around your neighborhood in case the dog lives nearby.
2. Take the dog to the nearest veterinarian or shelter to have the dog scanned for a microchip and checked for a tattoo.
3. Notify all the correct authorities to report the dog found. Call your local police (non-emergency line). Also, call your local animal control agency (ACO), to complete a found dog report or bring the dog to them if you are unable to keep the dog while researching for his/her owner.
4. Create "found dog" flyers and post them around the neighborhood and at animal service businesses.
5. Post on your local craigslist, in your local paper (found ads are often free) and on other lost and found Internet/Facebook sites.

Five Things to Do If You Have Lost or Found a Dog ©Lost Dogs of America. Lostdogsofamerica.org. This is a free service with articles & resources on finding a lost dog.

REMINDER: PREVENTION IS THE BEST ACTION PLAN!
KEEP YOUR DOG SAFE AND SECURE, AND UNDER YOUR WATCHFUL EYE.

PHONE NUMBERS EVERY DOG OWNER NEEDS

PRINT OUT THIS PAGE WITH THE PHONE NUMBERS AND ALWAYS KEEP HANDY.

EVERY DOG OWNER should keep these numbers on hand. Program them into your cell phone, include them in your dog's first aid kit, and keep a copy in your purse/wallet and the glove box of your car. Having these numbers at your fingertips could save your dog's life. Some of these services have a fee. Some are free. Stay safe.

MEDICAL EMERGENCY SUPPORT:

- **National Animal Poison Control Center (888) 426-4435.** This a 24-hour emergency hotline. There may be a fee.
- **Pet Poison Helpline (855) 764-7661.** (PetPoisonHelpline.com).
- **Emergency Disaster Hotline (800) 227-4645.** They connect you with valuable information and resources for pet owners affected by disasters: i.e. earthquakes, hurricanes, flooding, fire, and more.

LOST DOG SUPPORT:

- **National Pet Recovery Hotline (800) 984-8638.** A 24-hour service to help you locate your lost pet.
- **Pet Amber Alert (877) 875-7387.**
- **AKC Companion Animal Recovery (800) 252-7894.** Resources for lost dogs that are part of their registry.
- **Microchip.** Contact your dog's microchip company in case he gets lost, or to make changes to your contact information.
- **Stolen Pet Hotline 1-800-STOLEN-PET.**
- **Petfinder (800) 666-5678. (Petfinder.com).** A 24-hour lost and found service for members. Paid and free assistance.

PET LOSS SUPPORT:

- **Pet Loss Support Hotline (888) 478-7574.** A 24-hour hotline. Emotional support for those who've lost a pet.

DOG TRAINING SUPPORT:

- **Dog Training Hotline (212) 727-7257. (TheDogSite.com).** A free dog owners training, resource, and referral helpline provided by the American Dog Trainers Network.
- **Animal Behavior Hotline (312) 644-8338.** Free service to pet owners experiencing behavior issues with their dogs or cats.

PET TRAVEL SUPPORT:

- **Pet Travel Hotline 1-800-545-USDA.** Before traveling by plane with your dog, call with questions about transporting your pet, what papers you need to provide, what to bring, etc.
- **Pet Airways (888) 738-2479. (PetAirways.com).** Pet only airline.
- **Pet Travel Information (877) 241-0184. (PetTravel.com).** Worldwide resource for traveling with pets.

OTHER IMPORTANT NUMBERS:

- **Spay/Neuter Helpline 1-800-248-SPAY:** This is a National referral service to free or low cost spay and neuter services.
- **Animal Legal Hotline (707) 795-2533:** Call if you think someone is mistreating a dog or other animal or want to report a pet professional you think is acting illegally or unethically.

YOUR VET'S PHONE/ADDRESS: _____

_____

EMERGENCY VET PHONE/ADDRESS: _____

_____

Study the directions to your ER Vet Clinic so you can get there quickly.

PET WEBSITES EVERY DOG OWNER NEEDS

THESE ARE ONLY A SAMPLE of the amazing online sites available to pet owners. Have fun learning and pet shopping!

HEALTH:

- VetStreet.com - Pet owner resources/Pet Health and Wellness.
- PetMD.com - Massive compilation of pet health and wellness.
- Healthypet.com - American Animal Hospital Association.
- AVMA.org - American Veterinary Medical Association.
- AHVMA.org - American Holistic Veterinary Medical Association.
- Petsandparasites.org – Information/resources on parasites.
- PetPoisonHelpline.com (855) 764-7661

TRAINING

- AVSAB.org - American Veterinary Society of Animal Behavior.
- AKC.org - American Kennel Club. Dog Owners Resource Center.
- TheDogSite.com - The American Dog Trainers Network.
- Apdt.com - The Association of Professional Dog Trainers

LOST DOG SUPPORT

- PetAmberAlert.com
- Missinganimalresponse.com
- Lostdogsofamerica.com
- Helpinglostpets.com
- Lostcatfinder.com (In case you have a kitty).

PET ADOPTION/RESCUE

- AdoptaPet.com - Connects homeless pets with caring owners.
- PetFinder.com - Connects you with waiting to be adopted pets.
- AKC.org/akc-rescue-network/

MICROCHIP COMPANIES (There are other companies as well)

- Home Again - HomeAgain.com
- Avid - Avidid.com
- AKC Reunite - AKCReunite.org

FAVORITE PET SHOPPING SITES

- Chewy.com
- OnlyNaturalPet.com
- Petco.com
- PetsMart.com
- Amazon.com
- EntirelyPets.com
- IHeartDogs.com
- 1800PetMeds.com (Online pet pharmacy)
- WalmartPetRx.com (to order pet meds online)
- PetCare.RX Online Animal Pharmacy

GENERAL DOG CARE/LIFESTYLE

- PetDiets.com - Info on healthy dog diets (i.e. homemade).
- DogFoodAdvisor.com – Dog food reviews and advice.
- DogTime.com - Covers all things dogs.
- Dogsters.com - Educates on how to best care for your dog.
- ModernDogMagazine.com - Diverse topics/training tips.
- Rover.com - Connects you with quality dog sitting, dog walking, and at home boarding service.
- BringFido.com - Resource for pet and owner travel planning.
- PetTravel.com - Worldwide resource for traveling pets.
- PetAirways.com - Pet only airline.
- AKC.ORG - The American Kennel Club is a registry of pedigreed purebred dogs. They also offer resources for dog owners.
- DogBreedInfo.com - Educates dog owners about dog breeds.

PET INSURANCE COMPANIES (There are more to choose from)

- Figo – FigoPetInsurance.com
- Trupanion – Trupanion.com
- Healthy Paws – HealthyPawsPetInsurance.com
- Pets Best – PetsBest.com
- AKC – AKCPetInsurance.com
- Nationwide – PetInsurance.com

RECORD YOUR FAVORITE PET SHOPPING WEBSITES ON PAGE 100.

FAVORITE PET SHOPPING WEBSITES

MY LITTLE DOG - A HEARTBEAT AT MY FEET.

-EDITH WHARTON

NOTES

_____
_____
_____
_____
_____
_____
_____
_____
_____
_____
_____
_____
_____
_____
_____
_____
_____
_____
_____
_____
_____
_____
_____

MY GOAL IN LIFE IS TO BE AS GOOD A
PERSON AS MY DOG ALREADY THINKS I AM.

 —UNKNOWN

ABOUT THE AUTHOR

LEILA GRANDEMANGE is the author of several charming books, an award-winning writer, and recipient of the AKC Responsible Dog Ownership Public Service Award. She participates in various dog sports, has bred and shown numerous champions, and is recognized as an AKC Breeder of Merit.

Animals have always been part of her life. Whether cleaning horse stalls or caring for her dogs, Leila grew to appreciate the immense responsibility of sharing life with animals. Today, she writes to promote the responsible care of our furry friends and to Inspire comfort and joy in daily living!

To learn more about Leila and her books subscribe and follow at WWW.LEILAGRANDEMANGE.COM, AND ON AMAZON.

TAIL WAGGING THANKS to Dr. Virginia Nunez, DVM, and Dr. David Hernke, DVM, for sharing their veterinary expertise in this book!

Thanks for using this dog health record book!
PLEASE ADD A SHORT REVIEW ON AMAZON
and let others know what you thought.

Puppies ARE A GIFT FROM ABOVE, ENTRUSTED TO US LIKE PRECIOUS SEEDS. WE WATER THEM WITH PRAISE, PATIENCE, AND LOVE, AND WATCH THEM GROW INTO FULL BLOOM.

–LEILA GRANDEMANGE

ALSO IN THIS SERIES,
A FEMALE PINK COVER EDITION
ISBN: 978-0-9975658-5-0